DOVER MASTERWORKS

Art Masterpieces to Color

Impressionist, Modern Art, Famous American

Rendered by

Marty Noble and
Muncie Hendler

Dover Publications, Inc.
Mineola, New York

Bibliographical Note

Dover Masterworks: Art Masterpieces to Color: Impressionist, Modern Art, Famous American, first published by Dover Publications, Inc., in 2015, is a republication in one volume of the following previously published Dover books: *Dover Masterworks: Color Your Own Impressionist Paintings* (2013), rendered by Marty Noble, *Dover Masterworks: Color Your Own Modern Art Paintings* (2013), rendered by Muncie Hendler, and *Dover Masterworks: Color Your Own Famous American Paintings* (2013), rendered by Marty Noble.

This 2015 edition printed for Barnes & Noble, Inc., by Dover Publications, Inc.

International Standard Book Number
ISBN-13: 978-0-486-80556-6
ISBN-10: 0-486-80556-5

Manufactured in the United States by Courier Corporation

Note

Designed with the experienced colorist in mind, the *Dover Masterworks* series of coloring books showcases meticulously detailed renderings of some of the most enduring masterworks. Each painting is shown in full color on the inside covers for easy reference. Choose your media, and then follow the artist's color scheme for an accurate representation of the original work, or pick your own colors for a more personal touch. When you're finished coloring, the perforated pages make it easy to display your finished work. Captions on the reverse side of each plate identify the artist and the title of the work, date of composition, medium employed, and include interesting historical facts about the work.

Impressionist
Masterpieces

Plate 1
GUSTAVE CAILLEBOTTE (1848–1894)
Oarsmen, 1877
Oil on canvas. 37¾ x 45½ in.

French artist Gustave Caillebotte painted exquisite landscapes and portraits, but was best known for his scenes of urban life and the new Parisian boulevards of the mid-nineteenth century. Although Caillebotte was an engineer by trade, he had studied art at the École des Beaux-Arts in Paris, where he met Renoir, Monet, and Degas. He displayed his works at the 1876 Impressionist Exhibition and eventually became the chief organizer, promoter, and financial patron for future shows. A substantial inheritance from his father enabled him to purchase paintings from Cézanne, Morisot, Pissarro, and others. He left this extensive collection of Impressionist paintings to the French government after his death. *Oarsmen* is most notable for its unique use of perspective, which narrows the field of vision to include only the two rowers, while obscuring their facial features.

Plate 2
MARY CASSATT (1844–1926)
Hélène de Septeuil, ca. 1890
Pastel on paper. 25⅞ x 16½ in.

Mary Stevenson Cassatt was an American artist primarily known for her paintings of mothers and children. Although she was born in Allegheny, Pennsylvania, Cassatt spent most of her adult life in France. Greatly influenced by Edgar Degas, Cassatt was the only American—and one of only three women—officially associated with the Impressionists. The United States Postal Service issued two commemorative stamps in honor of Mary Cassatt. The first, appearing in 1966 pictured her painting *The Boating Party*. The second, appearing in 1988, pictured a portrait of the artist. The subject of *Hélène de Septeuil* is the daughter of an innkeeper in Septeuil, where Cassatt lived during the summers of 1889 and 1890.

Mary Stevenson Cassatt was an American artist primarily known for her paintings of mothers and children. Although she was born in Allegheny, Pennsylvania, Cassatt spent most of her adult life in France. Greatly influenced by Edgar Degas, Cassatt was the only American—and one of only three women—officially associated with the Impressionists. The United States Postal Service issued two commemorative stamps in honor of Mary Cassatt. The first, appearing in 1966 pictured her painting *The Boating Party*. The second, appearing in 1988, pictured a portrait of the artist. This painting is much beloved for the intimacy it depicts between a mother and her daughter, especially in the child's seeming pride and enjoyment in the care her mother is taking with her hair.

Plate 4
PAUL CÉZANNE (1839–1906)
Madame Cézanne in a Red Armchair, ca. 1877
Oil on canvas. 28½ x 22½ in.

French Post-Impressionist painter Paul Cézanne was the only son of a wealthy banker. His early works had a dark, somber tone that brightened after he began to paint outdoors with Pissarro in 1872. Dissatisfied with the Impressionists' sole reliance on light effects, Cezanne concentrated on the use of geometric form and construction. A prime influence on twentieth-century art, notably Cubism, Cézanne created effects of depth and solidity by varying the interaction of planes of paint, parallel brushstroke, and intense color. His compositions include portraits of himself and his family, over 200 still lifes, and many variations of L'Estaque and Mont Sainte-Victoire landscapes. The subject of this painting is Cézanne's wife, Hortense Fiquet. She was his most frequent model, appearing in almost thirty of his paintings.

Plate 5
PAUL CÉZANNE (1839–1906)
Still Life with Plaster Cupid, ca. 1894
Oil on paper mounted on panel. 27½ x 22½ in.

French Post-Impressionist painter Paul Cézanne was the only son of a wealthy banker. His early works had a dark, somber tone that brightened after he began to paint outdoors with Pissarro in 1872. Dissatisfied with the Impressionists' sole reliance on light effects, Cezanne concentrated on the use of geometric form and construction. A prime influence on twentieth-century art, notably Cubism, Cézanne created effects of depth and solidity by varying the interaction of planes of paint, parallel brushstroke, and intense color. His compositions include portraits of himself and his family, over 200 still lifes, and many variations of L'Estaque and Mont Sainte-Victoire landscapes. One of the last paintings he completed in his career, *Still Life with Plaster Cupid*, is especially notable for its abstract tendencies, which many claim heralded Cubist movement.

Plate 6
PAUL CÉZANNE (1839–1906)
The Card-Players, 1885–90
Oil on canvas. 18¾ x 22½ in.

French Post-Impressionist painter Paul Cézanne was the only son of a wealthy banker. His early works had a dark, somber tone that brightened after he began to paint outdoors with Pissarro in 1872. Dissatisfied with the Impressionists' sole reliance on light effects, Cézanne concentrated on the use of geometric form and construction. A prime influence on twentieth-century art, notably Cubism, Cézanne created effects of depth and solidity by varying the interaction of planes of paint, parallel brushstroke, and intense color. Cézanne painted five different versions of the scene depicted in *The Card-Players*, which shows a group of peasants playing cards. In all of the versions, he emphasizes the serious expressions of the players, each one concentrating intensely on the game.

Plate 7
EDGAR DEGAS (1834–1917)
Beach Scene, 1876-77
Oil on canvas. 18½ x 32½ in.

Born in Paris, France, Degas taught himself to paint by copying the Old Masters in the Louvre. He enrolled at the École des Beaux Arts and began to take an interest in painting modern life subjects. Degas painted the subtle movements of musicians, ballet dancers, and other stage performers in elegant, painstaking detail. These kinds of subjects afforded him the opportunity to depict fleeting moments in time and unusual angles. Akin to the view through the lens of a camera, Degas's paintings are infused with novel, unique perspectives that have come to epitomize his work. This painting, which depicts a nursemaid combing the hair of a young girl, was painted with the models posed in the artist's studio, and not on an actual beach.

Plate 8
EDGAR DEGAS (1834–1917)
Monsieur Perrot's Dance Class, ca. 1875
Oil on canvas. 33½ x 29½ in.

Born in Paris, France, Degas taught himself to paint by copying the Old Masters in the Louvre. He enrolled at the École des Beaux Arts and began to take an interest in painting modern life subjects. Degas painted the subtle movements of musicians, ballet dancers, and other stage performers in elegant, painstaking detail. These kinds of subjects afforded him the opportunity to depict fleeting moments in time and unusual angles. Akin to the view through the lens of a camera, Degas's paintings are infused with novel, unique perspectives that have come to epitomize his work. In this painting, the dancers in the foreground are not the main focus of attention. Instead, your eye is led diagonally from above, as if you're looking at the scene from the wings of the theater.

Born in Paris, France, Degas taught himself to paint by copying the Old Masters in the Louvre. He enrolled at the École des Beaux Arts and began to take an interest in painting modern life subjects. Degas painted the subtle movements of musicians, ballet dancers, and other stage performers in elegant, painstaking detail. These kinds of subjects afforded him the opportunity to depict fleeting moments in time and unusual angles. Akin to the view through the lens of a camera, Degas's paintings are infused with novel, unique perspectives that have come to epitomize his work. The subject of this work, Edmond Duranty, was a wealthy writer and art critic who founded a short-lived magazine. He was also an enthusiastic fan of Impressionism and counted many artists as his friends.

Plate 10
PAUL GAUGUIN (1848–1903)
The Four Breton Girls, ca. 1886
Oil on canvas. 28¼ x 36 in.

A major precursor of modern art, French artist Paul Gauguin pioneered an appreciation of the simple and primitive in art. Generally regarded as one of the greatest of the Post Impressionists, he depicted peasant life in Brittany early in his career and spent the last ten years of his life painting in Tahiti and the Marquesas Islands. His Breton style, characterized by flat contoured figures, gradually matured into the richly colored works of his later South Seas period. His Tahitian works—among his most famous—are comprised of native figures and landscapes, with strong outlines and flat, bold colors. *Four Breton Girls* was first exhibited at the Impressionists gallery in 1886, and shows Gauguin's use of more defined contours than was typical of his Impressionist contemporaries.

Plate 11
PAUL GAUGUIN (1848–1903)
Woman in the Waves (Ondine), 1889
Oil on canvas. 36¼ x 28¼ in.

A major precursor of modern art, French artist Paul Gauguin pioneered an appreciation of the simple and primitive in art. Generally regarded as one of the greatest of the Post Impressionists, he depicted peasant life in Brittany early in his career and spent the last ten years of his life painting in Tahiti and the Marquesas Islands. His Breton style, characterized by flat contoured figures, gradually matured into the richly colored works of his later South Seas period. His Tahitian works—among his most famous—are comprised of native figures and landscapes, with strong outlines and flat, bold colors. The image depicted in *Woman in the Waves* became a familiar motif for Gauguin, appearing in numerous works throughout his career.

Plate 12
PAUL GAUGUIN (1848–1903)
Two Tahitian Women with Mango Blossoms, 1899
Oil on canvas. 37 x 28½ in.

A major precursor of modern art, French artist Paul Gauguin pioneered an appreciation of the simple and primitive in art. Generally regarded as one of the greatest of the Post Impressionists, he depicted peasant life in Brittany early in his career and spent the last ten years of his life painting in Tahiti and the Marquesas Islands. His Breton style, characterized by flat contoured figures, gradually matured into the richly colored works of his later South Seas period. His Tahitian works—among his most famous—are comprised of native figures and landscapes, with strong outlines and flat, bold colors. This painting, which depicts two women from Tahiti, is part of the permanent collection of the Metropolitan Museum of Art.

Plate 13
VINCENT VAN GOGH (1853–1890)
Agostina Segatori Sitting in the Café du Tambourin, 1887
Oil on canvas. 21¾ x 18¼ in.

The Dutch Post-Impressionist painter tried such varied careers as language teacher, art dealer, and preacher before he began to paint in earnest in 1880. Expressive brushwork, the heightened use of color, and an intense emotionality typify van Gogh's unique style. His attempt to organize an artists' community in Arles with Toulouse-Lautrec and Gauguin proved to be unsuccessful. Van Gogh's volatile career lasted merely one decade; he took his own life in 1890. Although he sold just one painting during his lifetime, van Gogh produced 800 oil paintings and 700 drawings. The subject of this painting, Agostina Segatori, was the owner of the Café du Tambourin, and frequently allowed van Gogh to exchange paintings for meals when he was unable to pay.

The Dutch Post-Impressionist painter tried such varied careers as language teacher, art dealer, and preacher before he began to paint in earnest in 1880. Expressive brushwork, the heightened use of color, and an intense emotionality typify van Gogh's unique style. His attempt to organize an artists' community in Arles with Toulouse-Lautrec and Gauguin proved to be unsuccessful. Van Gogh's volatile career lasted merely one decade; he took his own life in 1890. Although he sold just one painting during his lifetime, van Gogh produced 800 oil paintings and 700 drawings. Van Gogh painted *The Man Is at Sea* from Virginie Demont-Breton's engraving, *Man at Sea* while living in Saint Paul asylum in Saint-Remy-de-Provence.

Plate 15
VINCENT VAN GOGH (1853–1890)
Portrait of the Postman Joseph Roulin, 1889
Oil on canvas. 25⅜ x 21¾ in.

The Dutch Post-Impressionist painter tried such varied careers as language teacher, art dealer, and preacher before he began to paint in earnest in 1880. Expressive brushwork, the heightened use of color, and an intense emotionality typify van Gogh's unique style. His attempt to organize an artists' community in Arles with Toulouse-Lautrec and Gauguin proved to be unsuccessful. Van Gogh's volatile career lasted merely one decade; he took his own life in 1890. Although he sold just one painting during his lifetime, van Gogh produced 800 oil paintings and 700 drawings. This painting was completed as part of a group of portraits that van Gogh painted of the Roulin family between 1888 and 1889.

French painter and printmaker Édouard Manet was the son of a high-ranking government official who denounced Manet's inclination toward art. Although Manet's art was strongly rooted in the classics, he was often criticized for his modernity. The Salon rejected several of his paintings due to their controversial subjects. Having adopted the style of painting out-of-doors, Manet was a greatly respected practitioner of Impressionism, though he did not participate in the official exhibitions of the group. Manet was one of the first nineteenth-century painters to spurn academic formulæ and subjects in favor of the depiction of contemporary life. In this painting, Manet depicts a working-class woman looking contemplative while drinking a glass of plum brandy and holding an unlit cigarette. It is often praised as exemplary of the independence that women were newly capable of during that period.

Plate 17
ÉDOUARD MANET (1832–1883)
Argenteuil, **1874**
Oil on canvas. 58½ x 45¼ in.

French painter and printmaker Édouard Manet was the son of a high-ranking government official who denounced Manet's inclination toward art. Although Manet's art was strongly rooted in the classics, he was often criticized for his modernity. The Salon rejected several of his paintings due to their controversial subjects. Having adopted the style of painting out-of-doors, Manet was a greatly respected practitioner of Impressionism, though he did not participate in the official exhibitions of the group. Manet was one of the first nineteenth-century painters to spurn academic formulæ and subjects in favor of the depiction of contemporary life. This painting depicts a young woman accompanied by a boater on the banks of the Seine at Argenteuil. Due to its naturalist subject and vibrant colors, *Argenteuil* is considered one of the first true Impressionist paintings.

Plate 18
ÉDOUARD MANET (1832–1883)
A Bar at the Folies-Bergère, 1881–82
Oil on canvas. 37¾ x 51¼ in.

French painter and printmaker Édouard Manet was the son of a high-ranking government official who denounced Manet's inclination toward art. Although Manet's art was strongly rooted in the classics, he was often criticized for his modernity. The Salon rejected several of his paintings due to their controversial subjects. Having adopted the style of painting out-of-doors, Manet was a greatly respected practitioner of Impressionism, though he did not participate in the official exhibitions of the group. Manet was one of the first nineteenth-century painters to spurn academic formulæ and subjects in favor of the depiction of contemporary life. The Folies-Bergère was one of the most elaborate variety-show halls in Paris. The woman standing behind the marble counter appears to be lost in thought, but in the reflection in the mirror behind her, she appears to be waiting on a customer.

Leading French Impressionist Claude Monet was introduced to the *plein air* style of painting in the 1860s by Boudin. Monet sought to record the "impression" that the subject gave the viewer at that precise time of day, effectively capturing the transient effects of light. Beginning in 1890, he embarked on a series of works that studied the same subject under different light conditions. These works include *Haystacks* and *Water Lilies*, both of which express the subtle nuances of color, light, and atmosphere. Monet spent the summer of 1867 in the resort town of Sainte-Adresse on the English Channel, where he painted this picture. Monet's father is seated next to his niece. Monet's cousin and her father stand together at the garden fence.

Plate 20
CLAUDE MONET (1840–1926)
Villas at Bordighera, 1884
Oil on canvas. 45¼ x 51⅓ in.

Leading French Impressionist Claude Monet was introduced to the *plein air* style of painting in the 1860s by Boudin. Monet sought to record the "impression" that the subject gave the viewer at that precise time of day, effectively capturing the transient effects of light. Beginning in 1890, he embarked on a series of works that studied the same subject under different light conditions. These works include *Haystacks* and *Water Lilies*, both of which express the subtle nuances of color, light, and atmosphere. The subject of this painting is the garden of Mr. Moreno in the Italian villa of Bordighera, a place Monet described as an "earthly paradise."

Plate 21
CLAUDE MONET (1840–1926)
La Japonaise (Camille Monet in Japanese costume),
1875–76
Oil on canvas. 91¼ x 56 in.

Leading French Impressionist Claude Monet was introduced to the *plein air* style of painting in the 1860s by Boudin. Monet sought to record the "impression" that the subject gave the viewer at that precise time of day, effectively capturing the transient effects of light. Beginning in 1890, he embarked on a series of works that studied the same subject under different light conditions. These works include *Haystacks* and *Water Lilies*, both of which express the subtle nuances of color, light, and atmosphere. Though he never went to Japan, Monet was fascinated with the country and its art. The woman in this painting is Monet's first wife, Camille.

Plate 22
BERTHE MORISOT (1841–1895)
Hide and Seek, 1873
Oil on canvas. 17¾ x 21⅝ in.

Born in Bourges, France, Morisot was the daughter of a high-ranking government official and granddaughter of the Rococo painter Jean-Honoré Fragonard. As a child, she knew she wanted to be an artist, and learned to draw by copying works in the Louvre with her sister. Exhibiting regularly with the Impressionists, Morisot was influenced by the work of Édouard Manet, and eventually married his younger brother, Eugene, in 1874. Her paintings usually depicted members of her family, including her daughter, Julie. Among her closest friends were Degas, Renoir, and Monet. In *Hide and Seek*, Morisot depicts her sister Edma and niece Jeanne playing together in the country. This painting is typical of the female Impressionists in its focus on the relationship between a mother and her child.

Plate 23
BERTHE MORISOT (1841–1895)
On the Veranda, 1884
Oil on canvas. 31⅞ x 39⅜ in.

Born in Bourges, France, Morisot was the daughter of a high-ranking government official and granddaughter of the Rococo painter Jean-Honoré Fragonard. As a child, she knew she wanted to be an artist, and learned to draw by copying works in the Louvre with her sister. Exhibiting regularly with the Impressionists, Morisot was influenced by the work of Édouard Manet, and eventually married his younger brother, Eugene, in 1874. Her paintings usually depicted members of her family, including her daughter, Julie. Among her closest friends were Degas, Renoir, and Monet. Like many of Morisot's paintings, *On the Veranda* depicts a young girl engaged in a private moment. It is notable for Morisot's use of color in contrasting the girl's vibrant red hair against the blues and greens of the countryside through the window.

Plate 24
CAMILLE PISSARRO (1830–1903)
Chestnut Trees at Louveciennes, ca. 1872
Oil on canvas. 16⅛ x 21¼ in.

One of the founders of Impressionism, Pissarro studied art in Paris, where he was first attracted to the works of the Barbizon school and the realism of Corot. In the 1860s and 1870s, Pissarro lightened his palette and applied brushstrokes of bright color on his canvases to create luminous effects. Along with fellow Impressionist painters Monet, Renoir, and Manet, Pissarro helped organize the first independent Impressionist exhibition in 1874. He also experimented with various artistic styles, such as Pointillism, a technique popularized by Seurat. In this painting, a parent and child are bundled up against the cold, and are embraced by the arched branches of the chestnut trees above them. Although their faces are not clearly detailed, the woman may be Pissarro's wife, Julie, and their six-year-old daughter Minette.

Plate 25
CAMILLE PISSARRO (1830–1903)
The Old Marketplace in Rouen and
the Rue de l'Epicerie, **1898**
Oil on canvas. 31¾ x 25½ in.

One of the founders of Impressionism, Pissarro studied art in Paris, where he was first attracted to the works of the Barbizon school and the realism of Corot. In the 1860s and 1870s, Pissarro lightened his palette and applied brushstrokes of bright color on his canvases to create luminous effects. Along with fellow Impressionist painters Monet, Renoir, and Manet, Pissarro helped organize the first independent Impressionist exhibition in 1874. He also experimented with various artistic styles, such as Pointillism, a technique popularized by Seurat. Due to concerns with his health, Pissarro preferred to paint indoors, often choosing subjects that he could view from a window. He painted this particular vantage point of the Rue de l'Epicerie three times, though only once while the market was in progress.

Born in France, Renoir began his art career with an apprenticeship at a factory, where he painted flowers onto porcelain dishes. Along with fellow Impressionist painters Sisley, Bazille, and Monet, Renoir painted landscapes directly from nature to study the effects of light. Using feathery brushstrokes and sparkling bursts of color, Renoir painted over 2,000 portraits in his lifetime. Among his favorite subjects were portraits of women, children, and social scenes of everyday life, as pictured in his *Luncheon of the Boating Party.* This painting is noted for its rich color harmonies and the delicate arrangement of luxurious objects. The picture hanging in the background is Manet's etched reproduction of *Little Cavaliers* by Diego Velázquez.

Born in France, Renoir began his art career with an apprenticeship at a factory, where he painted flowers onto porcelain dishes. Along with fellow Impressionist painters Sisley, Bazille, and Monet, Renoir painted landscapes directly from nature to study the effects of light. Using feathery brushstrokes and sparkling bursts of color, Renoir painted over 2,000 portraits in his lifetime. Among his favorite subjects were portraits of women, children, and social scenes of everyday life, as pictured in his *Luncheon of the Boating Party*. The subject of this painting is Mademoiselle Leclere; it was painted in Monet's garden at Argenteuil.

Plate 28
PIERRE-AUGUSTE RENOIR (1841–1919)
At the Concert, 1880
Oil on canvas. 39 x 31½ in.

Born in France, Renoir began his art career with an apprenticeship at a factory, where he painted flowers onto porcelain dishes. Along with fellow Impressionist painters Sisley, Bazille, and Monet, Renoir painted landscapes directly from nature to study the effects of light. Using feathery brushstrokes and sparkling bursts of color, Renoir painted over 2,000 portraits in his lifetime. Among his favorite subjects were portraits of women, children, and social scenes of everyday life, as pictured in his *Luncheon of the Boating Party*. *At the Concert* was Renoir's last in a series of paintings that depicted elegant figures in theater boxes. The painting originally featured a male figure in the upper-right corner, which was removed before Renoir finished the work.

French Post-Impressionist and theorist Paul Sérusier was one of the co-founders of the Symbolist Nabis in the 1890s. A student of philosophy, Sérusier decided to become an artist and enrolled at the Académie Julian in Paris. He met Gauguin in Brittany at Pont-Aven in 1888, painting for a time in the manner of Synthetism. In 1897, he joined the school of religious art at the Benedictine abbey of Beuron in Germany. Powerfully affected by their themes of religious symbolism and proportions, Sérusier gravitated toward a mystical conception of art. He published his *ABC of Painting* in 1921, which concerned systems of proportion and color relationships. This painting depicts the chapel of Notre-Dame-de-Portes in the French commune of Châteauneuf-du-Faou, where Sérusier lived for several years. It currently resides in the collection of the Musée des Beaux Arts at Quimper.

Plate 30
ALFRED SISLEY (1839–1899)
The Bridge at Villeneuve-la-Garenne, 1872
Oil on canvas. 19½ x 25¾ in.

An originator of French Impressionism, Alfred Sisley was born in Paris, the son of well-to-do English parents living in France. From 1857 to 1862, he studied in London, where his interest in art blossomed. Returning to Paris, Sisley entered the studio of Charles Gleyre, where he engendered friendships with Monet, Bazille, and Renoir. He painted landscapes almost exclusively, paying unusual attention to detail and light effects. Sisley painted a second work showing the bridge at Villeneuve-la-Garenne, which is now located at the Fogg Art Museum in Massachusetts. His use of flat, rectangular brushstrokes, which can be seen in the surface of the water, was typical of early Impressionist paintings.

Modern Art
Masterpieces

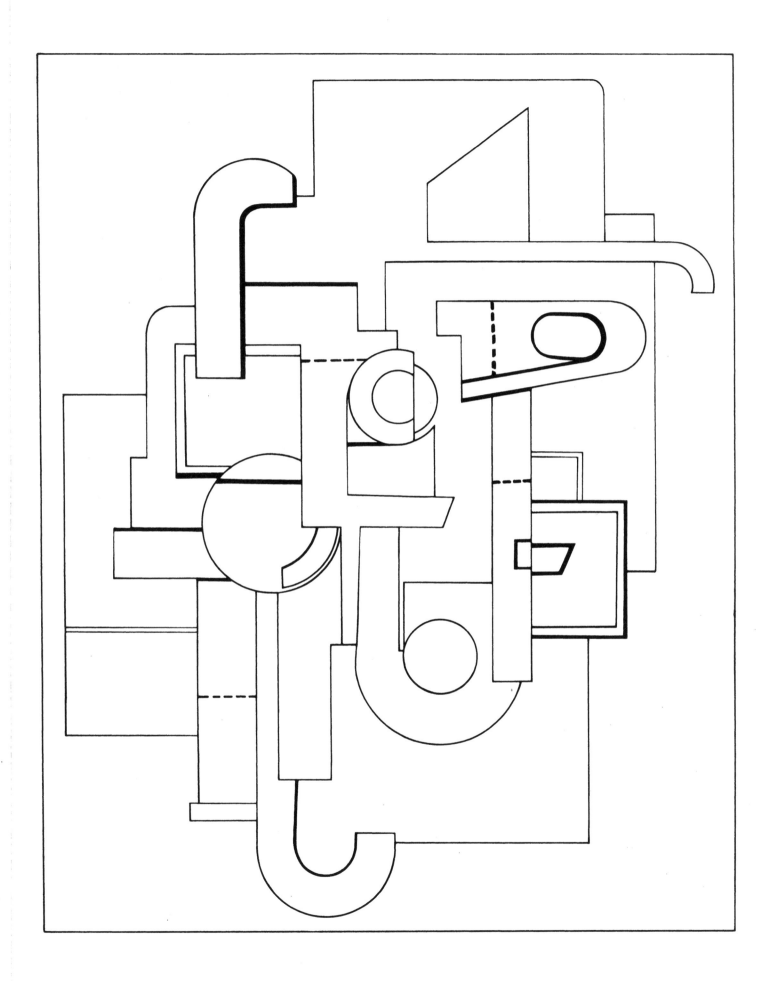

Plate 31
WILLI BAUMEISTER (1889–1955)
Gouachemalning, **1923**

One of the most important German painters of the modern era, Willi Baumeister apprenticed as a decorative painter before beginning his artistic studies at the Royal Academy of Stuttgart in 1907. His work first began to attract attention during World War I, though he did not gain an international reputation until Fernand Léger and Le Corbusier helped spread his work throughout Europe in 1922. Baumeister was prohibited by the Nazis from showing his work in Germany, though he was widely exhibited in London and Paris from 1933 until the end of World War II. This piece is typical of Baumeister's work during the early and mid-1920s, in its abstract representation of man and machines, in which the actual subject is almost completely unrecognizable beyond the painting's geometric shapes.

Plate 32
GEORGES BRAQUE (1882–1963)
La Guitariste, 1917

Georges Braque was a French painter and sculptor, and one of the first artists (along with Pablo Picasso) to paint in the Cubist style. Born in Argenteuil, France, Braque was raised in Le Havre, where he studied painting at the École des Beaux-Arts. Before his work in the development of Cubism, Braque painted in both the Impressionist and Fauvist styles, exhibiting his work alongside such artists as Henri Matisse, André Derain, and Paul Cézanne. This painting features a musician with a guitar, reduced to simplified geometric form; it is a typical example of Braque's work from this period.

Plate 33
MARC CHAGALL (1887–1985)
The Birthday, 1915

Russian-born painter and designer Marc Chagall developed a highly individual and personalized style, incorporating elements of Russian Expressionism, Surrealism, and Cubism. A unique blend of reality and dreams, his art is suffused with poetic imagery and striking visual metaphors. Most of his subject matter is rooted in the Russian-Jewish folklore of his childhood. His recurring motifs, such as rooftop fiddlers and floating brides, possess a surrealistic quality and frequently appear in a dreamlike setting. In his work, richly colored figures predominate within a loosely related series of images, providing a visual montage of Chagall's own life experiences. The subject of this painting is the artist and his bride-to-be, Bella. Painted just a few weeks before their wedding, this work is now in the collection of the Museum of Modern Art in New York.

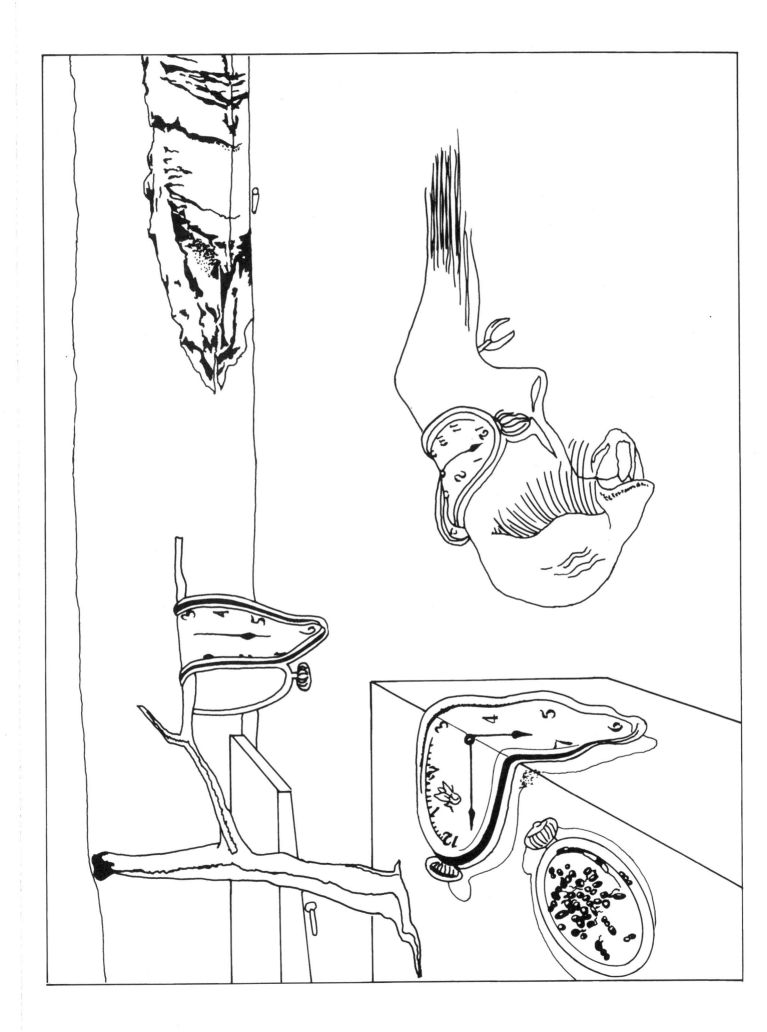

Plate 34
SALVADOR DALÍ (1904–1989)
The Persistence of Memory, 1935

Spanish painter Salvador Dalí studied at the Academy of Fine Arts in Madrid before moving to Paris. As a member of the Surrealist movement, Dalí promoted the idea of absurdity and the role of the unconscious in his art. Influenced by the psychoanalytic theories of Freud and abnormal psychology in general, he developed a range of unforgettable imagery, including distortions of the human form and limp watches, as seen in *The Persistence of Memory,* Dalí's most well-known painting. He also painted religious themes as well as numerous portraits of his wife. This painting resides in the collection of the Museum of Modern Art in New York.

Plate 35
STUART DAVIS (1892–1964)
Visa, 1951

Stuart Davis was born in 1892 into an artistic family, with his father serving as the art editor for the Philadelphia Press, and his mother working as a prominent sculptor. Davis worked in many different styles and genres, though he is most remembered as one of the earliest American modernist painters to experiment with pop art. In *Visa,* Davis composes the painting around a number of seemingly unrelated words, which he chose based as much on their aesthetic appeal as their meaning. While the central word—"Champion"—came from a matchbook-cover advertisement for spark plugs, the rest of the word choices are much more enigmatic. Additionally, he refused on several occasions to explain the title of the piece, saying only that it was "a secret because I believe in magic."

Plate 36
ANDRÉ DERAIN (1880–1954)
Westminster Bridge, 1906

A major exponent of the Fauvist movement, Derain was born in Chatou, France. His style closely resembles Matisse and Vlaminck, with whom he shared a studio. Derain was one of the first artists to collect African art, which became a key source of inspiration for many early-twentieth-century artists. Influenced by the work of Cézanne as well as the early Cubist paintings of Picasso and Braque, Derain continued to experiment with different compositional techniques. Westminster Bridge, considered one of the finest examples of Fauvist painting, was one of 30 works that Derain painted during his two trips to London in 1906. It currently resides in the collection of the Musée d'Orsay in Paris.

Born to Italian parents in Volos, Greece, Giorgio de Chirico is best remembered as the founder of the *scuola metafisica* movement, which was extremely influential for Salvador Dalí and other surrealists. Giorgio de Chirico studied under Georgios Rios in Athens and at the Academy of Fine Arts in Munich before returning to his ancestral home in Italy in 1909. It was there that de Chirico produced the bulk of his most famous paintings, during what is known as his metaphysical period, lasting from 1909 to 1919. At the height of this period, de Chirico painted *The Evil Genius of a King*, which appears to be a group of children's toys which defy gravity as they sit suspended on a tilted plane.

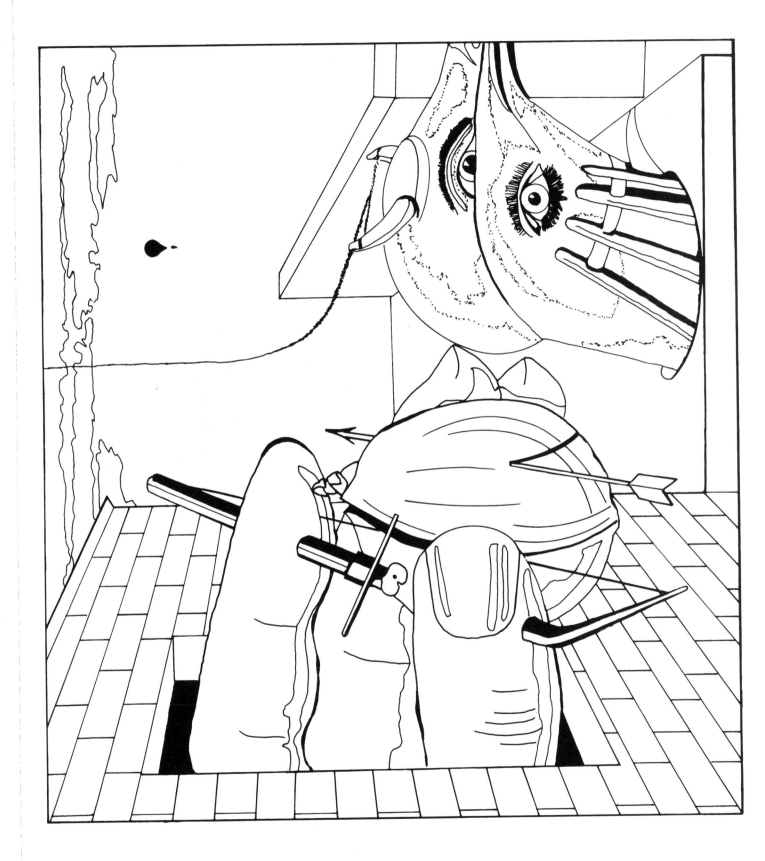

Plate 38
MAX ERNST (1891–1976)
Oedipus Rex, 1922

Born in Brühl, Germany, in 1891, Max Ernst was a prolific painter, sculptor, and poet, best remembered as a leading figure in both the Dada and Surrealist movements. Although he began producing art in 1909 while studying at the University of Bonn, Ernst's career as an artist truly began after returning to Cologne following four years in the military during World War I. Ernst was greatly influenced by the work of Giorgio de Chirico, Pablo Picasso, and Paul Gauguin, as well as contemporaries like Paul Klee. Ernst produced *Oedius Rex* while living in Cologne, shortly after forming the German Dada group with Jean Arp and Alfred Grunwald. The grotesque imagery and surreal composition are typical of Ernst's work from that period, and helped to make this painting one of the foundational works of the Dada movement.

Plate 39
JUAN GRIS (1887–1927)
Still Life with a Guitar, 1914

Born in Madrid, Spain, in 1887, Juan Gris spent the majority of his life and career in France, achieving great success as both a painter and sculptor. Although he began his career as a satirical cartoonist, he is best remembered for his work in the Cubist genre. After moving to Paris in 1906, Gris befriended Henri Matisse, Georges Braque, and Fernand Léger, each of whom had a great influence on his work. Gris greatly admired Pablo Picasso, and although the two are often associated together, it is believed that Picasso did not think much of Gris or his work. In this painting, common objects like a guitar, wine glass, and newspaper, are depicted in Gris's typical Cubist style. *Still Life with a Guitar* resides in the collection of the Metropolitan Museum of Art in New York.

Plate 40
MARSDEN HARTLEY (1877–1943)
Portrait of a German, **1914**

The youngest of nine children, Marsden Hartley was born and raised in Lewiston, Maine, and trained as an artist at the Cleveland Institute of Art, the New York School of Art, and the National Academy of Design. Inspired by the paintings of Albert Pinkham Ryder and the writings of Walt Whitman, Henry David Thoreau, and Ralph Waldo Emerson, Hartley viewed his art as a spiritual journey, through which he endeavored to express the essence of nature. His work had a profound influence on American Modernism, though he was also an important figure in the Regionalism movement as well. Hartley painted *Portrait of a German,* one of his most vivid abstractions, while living in Berlin during the early years of the First World War. It is currently in the collection of the Metropolitan Museum of Art in New York.

Plate 41
AUGUSTE HERBIN (1882–1960)
Vein, 1953

Born and raised in Quiévy, France, Auguste Herbin studied at the École des Beaux-Arts de Lille before moving to Paris in 1901. Although his early works display a great deal of influence by the Impressionists and Post-Impressionists, Herbin is best remembered for his later work, which show a transition from Cubism to a more abstract, geometrical style. Like many of his later paintings, the composition of *Vein* is based on a complex system, set forth in his 1949 book *L'Art Non-Figuratif Non-Objectif*, which forms correspondences between specific colors, forms, letters, and musical notes.

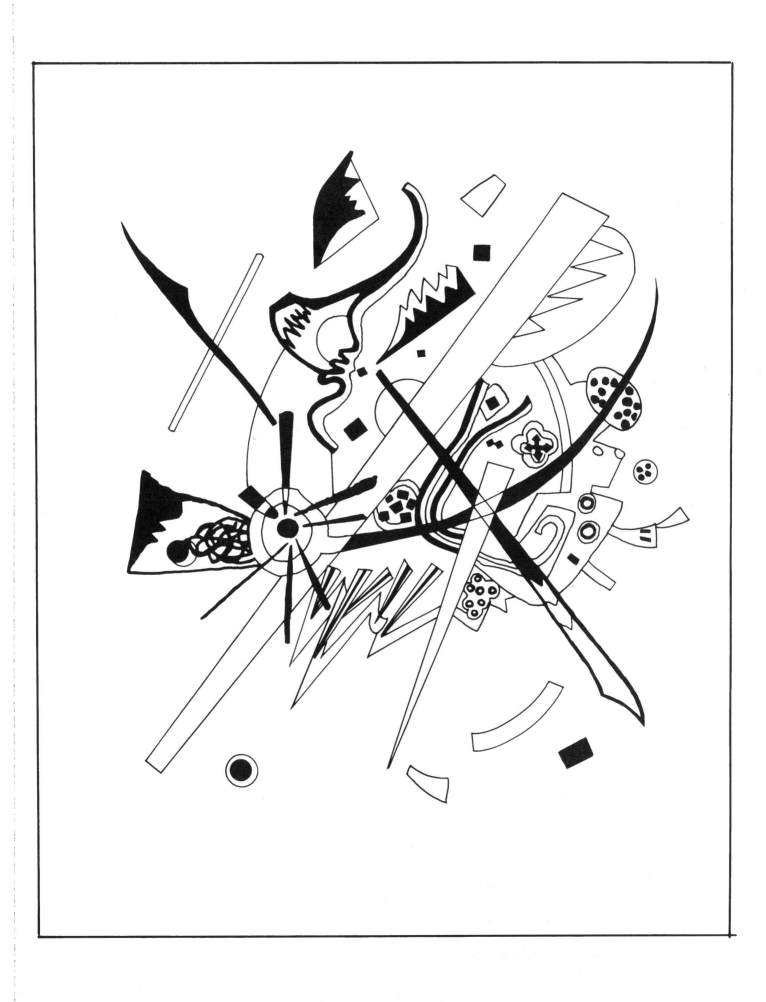

Plate 42
WASSILY KANDINSKY (1866–1944)
Kleine Welten I, 1922

Although he is best remembered as the first painter of purely abstract works, Russian artist Wassily Kandinsky originally made a name for himself as an Impressionist painter, greatly influenced by the work of Claude Monet. His transition into abstraction began while studying at the Academy of Fine Arts in Munich, though he would not begin the starkly geometric abstract paintings for which he is best known until almost ten years later. *Kleine Welten I* is the first in a series of twelve prints, six lithographs, four drypoints, and two woodcuts. "Kleine Welten" literally translates as "Small Worlds."

Plate 43
PAUL KLEE (1879–1940)
Clown, 1927

Born in Münchenbuchsee, Switzerland, in 1879, Paul Klee is considered one of the greatest Swiss painters of the modern era. Klee was greatly influenced by Expressionism, Cubism, and Surrealism, as well as by the Bauhaus school, where he worked alongside Wassily Kandinsky. Klee gained international success as an artist after his experiments with pure abstraction became popular throughout Europe during World War I. This painting, which depicts a Cubist representation of a clown, was typical of Klee's Bauhaus period in its use of rich, dark colors and inclusion of abstract graphical elements.

Plate 44
PAUL KLEE (1879–1940)
Figure in a Garden, 1937

Born in Münchenbuchsee, Switzerland, in 1879, Paul Klee is considered one of the greatest Swiss painters of the modern era. Klee was greatly influenced by Expressionism, Cubism, and Surrealism, as well as by the Bauhaus school, where he worked alongside Wassily Kandinsky. Klee gained international success as an artist after his experiments with pure abstraction became popular throughout Europe during World War I. Like many of Klee's paintings from the later years of his life, *Figure in a Garden* uses fragmented figures with little detail to express a whimsy that is quite different from the melancholy which was typical of his earlier works.

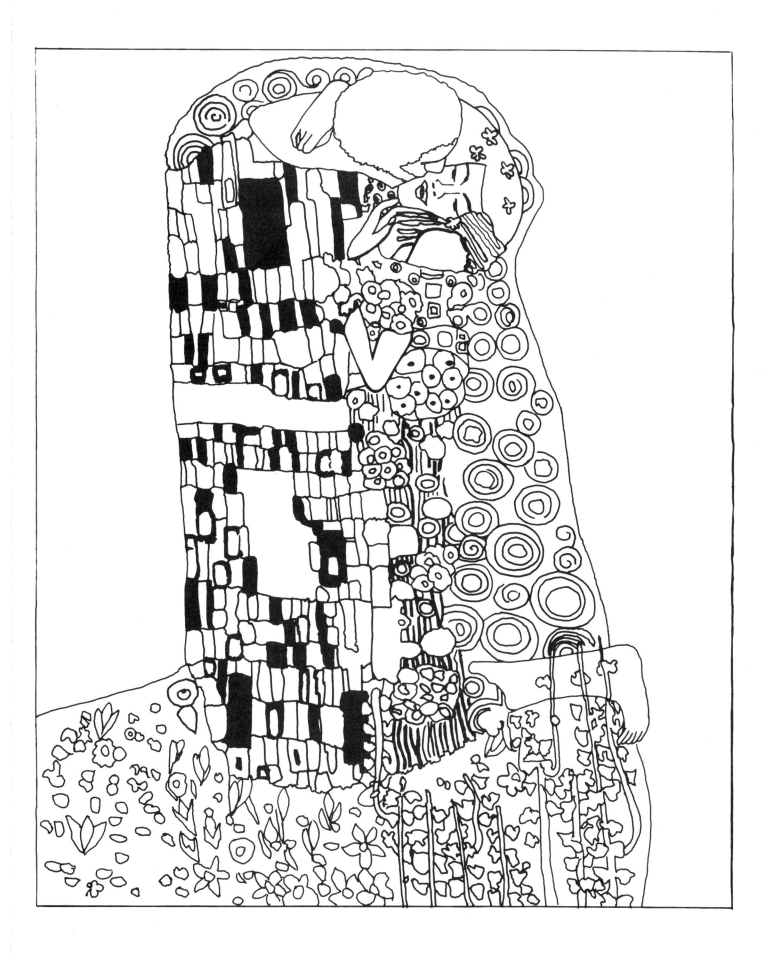

Plate 45
GUSTAV KLIMT (1862–1918)
The Kiss, **1908**

Born in Baumgarten, Austria, painter Gustav Klimt was one of the most well-known members of the Vienna Secession movement, which encouraged artists to revolt against academic art in favor of more decorative styles, such as Art Nouveau. Klimt was primarily a decorator, but he also produced murals and a number of portraits, as well as allegorical and mythical paintings. His work had a profound impact on Oskar Kokoschka and Egon Schiele. *The Kiss* is one of Klimt's most famous works. In it, a mass of patterns and shapes dominate his representation of a kissing couple.

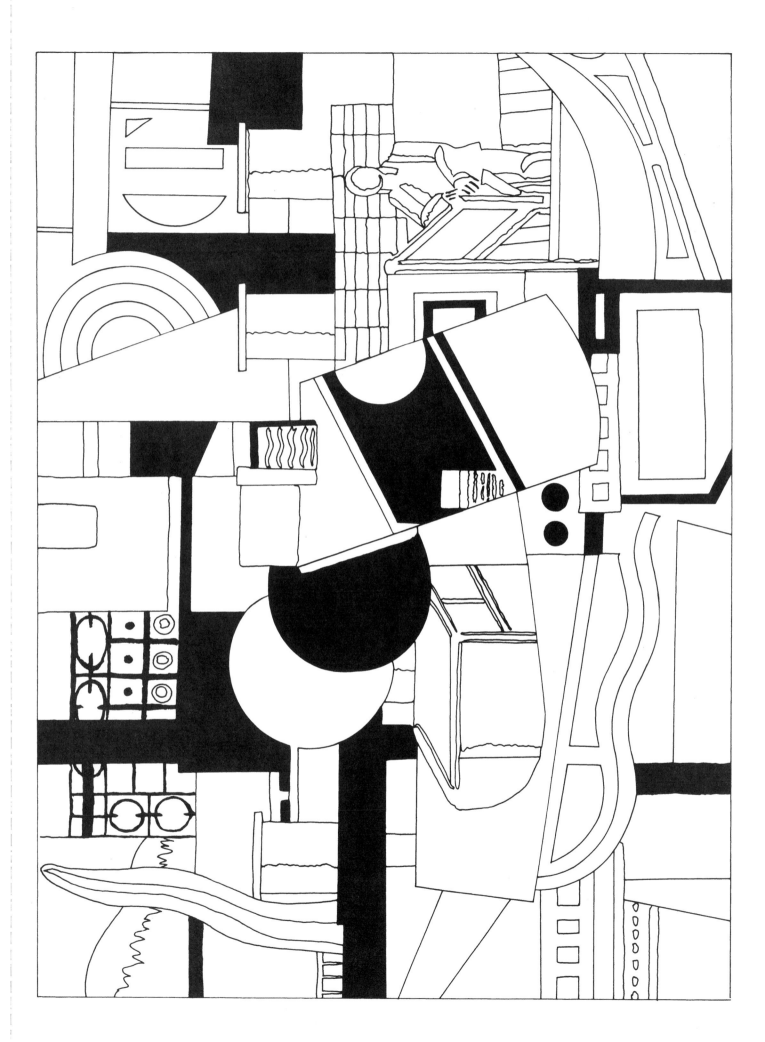

Plate 46
FERNAND LÉGER (1881–1955)
The Deck of the Tugboat, 1920

Born the son of a cattle farmer in Argenta, France, Fernand Léger apprenticed as an architect for two years before moving to Paris in 1900. There, he studied painting at the School of Decorative Arts and the École des Beaux-Arts, while supporting himself as a draftsman at a nearby architectural firm. Greatly influenced by the work of Cézanne and the Cubists, Léger would go on to form his own unique style of Cubism, characterized by machine-like elements and tubular forms. This style, nicknamed "tubism" and often referred to as "machine art" can be readily seen in the mechanistic shapes and forms that comprise *The Deck of the Tugboat.*

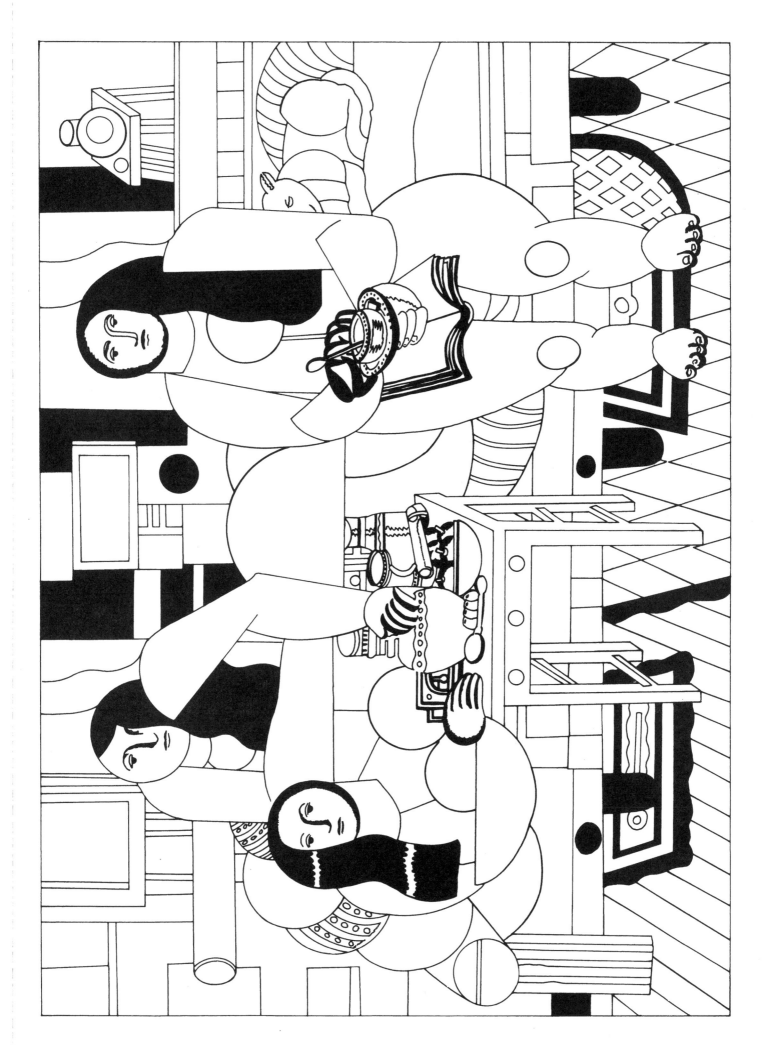

Plate 47
FERNAND LÉGER (1881–1955)
Three Women, 1921

Born the son of a cattle farmer in Argenta, France, Fernand Léger apprenticed as an architect for two years before moving to Paris in 1900. There, Léger studied painting at the School of Decorative Arts and the École des Beaux-Arts, while supporting himself as a draftsman at a nearby architectural firm. Greatly influenced by the work of Cézanne and the Cubists, Léger would go on to form his own unique style of Cubism, characterized my machine-like elements and tubular forms. Although the subject of *Three Women* is a group of reclining nudes sipping coffee in an apartment, his "machine art" style can still be observed in the mechanistic way the three subjects are depicted.

Plate 48
FRANZ MARC (1880–1916)
Blue Horse, **1911**

The son of a professional landscape painter, Franz Marc was born and raised in Munich, where he studied painting at the Academy of Fine Arts. Marc is best known as one of the most important artists in the German Expressionist movement, and as a founding member of the Expressionist artists' group known as *The Blue Ryder. Blue Horse* is typical of Marc's work during his association with *The Blue Ryder* in its simple, almost Cubist depiction of animal life and its bold use of primary colors.

Plate 49
HENRI MATISSE (1869–1954)
The Piano Lesson, 1916

French artist Henri Matisse abandoned his early studies in law to attend the Académie Julian and the École des Beaux-Arts in Paris when he was in his early twenties. Matisse, the most famous representative of the art movement known as Fauvism, used bold color to stir the emotions of viewers. The Fauvists created innovative works of vivid intensity through their use of pure color. Matisse's later works included more abstraction, as in his collages of colored paper cutouts. *The Piano Lesson* depicts a scene in Matisse's living room at his home in Issy-les-Moulineaux. The boy at the piano is the artist's eldest son, Pierre.

Plate 50
JOAN MIRÓ (1893–1983)
The Swallow of Love, 1934

Born in Barcelona, Joan Miró manifested an inclination toward art early in life. He studied at the La Lonja School of Fine Arts, where one of his instructors called his attention to Catalan primitive art—an influence that continued throughout his career. Although his early works reflect the influences of Cézanne, van Gogh, Cubism, and Fauvism, Miró soon allied himself firmly with the Surrealist movement. His work underwent a long and complex development, but some common elements include the bold use of color and curvilinear shapes. He also produced collages, ceramics, murals, etchings, and lithographs. *The Swallow of Love* is one of Miró's most recognizable paintings. It resides in the collection of the Museum of Modern Art in New York.

Plate 51
JOAN MIRÓ (1893–1983)
The Harlequin's Carnival, **1925**

Born in Barcelona, Joan Miro manifested an inclination toward art early in life. He studied at the La Lonja School of Fine Arts, where one of his instructors called his attention to Catalan primitive art—an influence that continued throughout his career. Although his early works reflect the influences of Cézanne, van Gogh, Cubism and Fauvism, Miró soon allied himself firmly with the Surrealist movement. His work underwent a long and complex development, but some common elements include the bold use of color and curvilinear shapes. He also produced collages, ceramics, murals, etchings, and lithographs. One of the artist's most clearly surrealist works, *The Harlequin's Carnival* is filled with pictorial symbols that Miró used, in his own words, "to deepen the magical side of things."

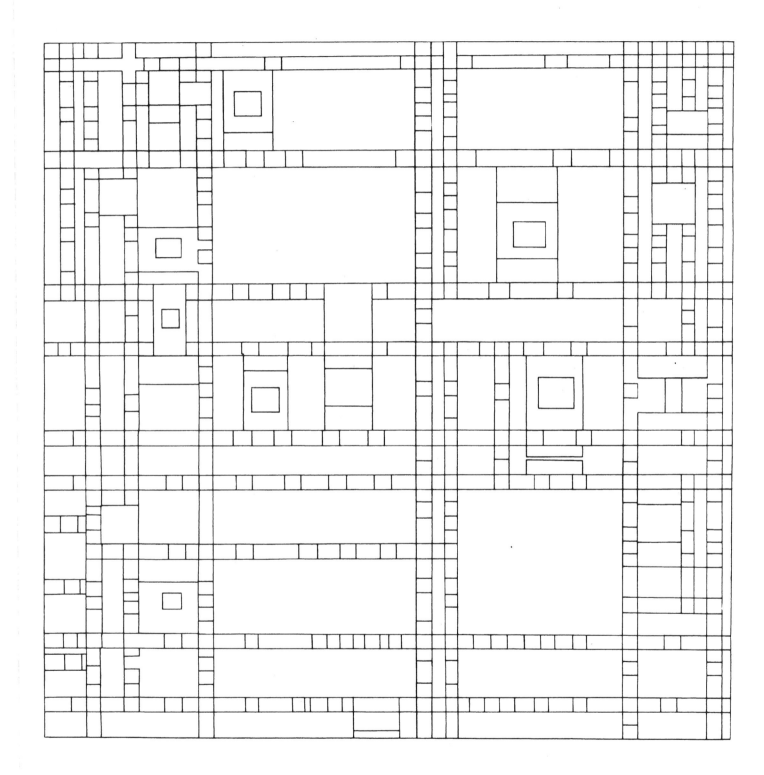

Plate 52
PIET MONDRIAN (1872–1944)
Broadway Boogie Woogie, 1943

A pioneer of abstract art, Dutch painter Piet Mondrian came from an artistic family. After moving to Paris in 1909, his work was greatly influenced by Cubism, and with time, Mondrian's compositions became increasingly more abstract. His first abstract paintings were composed of rhythmical horizontals and verticals, followed by those with geometrical grid patterns. After 1920, he began to paint pictures of colored rectangles with black outlines, a trend that enabled him to focus on the beauty of the simple relationships between pure colors. In *Broadway Boogie Woogie,* tiny blocks of brilliant color create a pulsing rhythm that jumps from one intersection to another, mimicking the vitality of a New York City street.

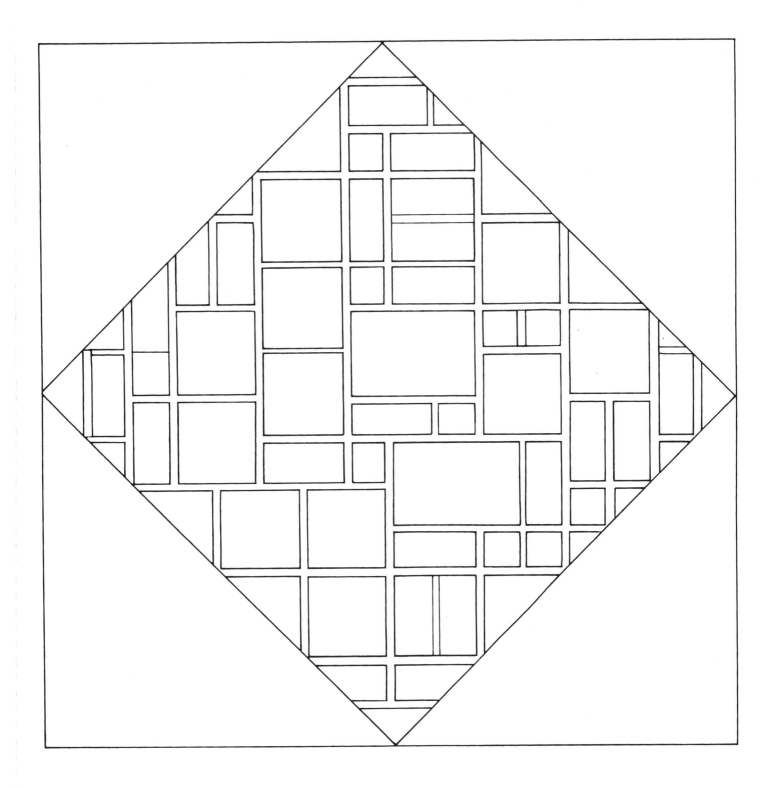

Plate 53
PIET MONDRIAN (1872–1944)
Composition with Grid VII, 1919

A pioneer of abstract art, Dutch painter Piet Mondrian came from an artistic family. After moving to Paris in 1909, his work was greatly influenced by Cubism, and with time, Mondrian's compositions became increasingly more abstract. His first abstract paintings were composed of rhythmical horizontals and verticals, followed by those with geometrical grid patterns. After 1920, he began to paint pictures of colored rectangles with black outlines, a trend that enabled him to focus on the beauty of the simple relationships between pure colors. *Composition with Grid VII* is one of Mondrian's earliest grid paintings, painted shortly after his return to Paris after World War I.

Plate 54
EDVARD MUNCH (1863–1944)
The Scream, 1893

A forerunner of the Expressionists, Norwegian artist Edvard Munch studied at the Oslo Academy, and then traveled to Paris, where he was largely influenced by the Symbolists and Gauguin. As with many artists, a lot of Munch's subject matter was drawn directly from his own life experiences. He produced intensely powerful images that often portrayed fear, anxiety, love, and death. *The Scream* is one of the best-known images in the history of art, and embodies the stress and angst of modern life. It is in the collection of the Munch Museum in Oslo, Norway.

Plate 55
PABLO PICASSO (1881–1973)
Three Musicians, 1921

Spanish artist Pablo Picasso was one of the most inventive painters of the twentieth century. Through his extraordinary imagination and prolific output, Picasso greatly contributed to many disparate styles and major artistic movements. Although he is most famous for his canvases, he also produced outstanding sculptures, ceramics, graphics, and book illustrations. *Three Musicians* is one of two similar collage and oil paintings completed by Picasso during a stay in Fontainebleau, France, in 1921. The figures Picasso depicts in this work are a Harlequin, a Pierrot, and a monk. The version presented here resides in the collection of the Museum of Modern Art in New York.

Plate 56
PABLO PICASSO (1881–1973)
Girl Before a Mirror, **1932**

Spanish artist Pablo Picasso was one of the most inventive painters of the twentieth century. Through his extraordinary imagination and prolific output, Picasso greatly contributed to many disparate styles and major artistic movements. Although he is most famous for his canvases, he also produced outstanding sculptures, ceramics, graphics, and book illustrations. The subject of this painting is Picasso's young mistress, Marie-Thérèse Walter, whom Picasso painted many times throughout the 1930s. *Girl Before a Mirror* was inspired by Édouard Manet's famous painting, *Before the Mirror,* which also depicts a woman gazing at her own reflection.

Plate 57
HENRI ROUSSEAU (1844–1910)
The Sleeping Gypsy, 1897

A customs officer who painted in his spare time, the French-born Rousseau had no formal artistic training, and only devoted himself exclusively to painting after his early retirement at the age of forty. Renowned for his highly stylized works, Rousseau created detailed paintings of lush foliage and mysterious figures in exotic imaginary landscapes. His portraits, still lifes, and junglescapes are examples of a manner of painting known as "naïve," a term indicative of the way an artist treated a subject in his or her own visionary way. *The Sleeping Gypsy* depicts a lion passing a sleeping woman on a moonlit night. One of the most recognizable paintings of the twentieth century, it resides in the collection of the Museum of Modern Art in New York.

Originally intending to be an architect, Signac began to paint under the guidance of Monet and Guillaumin in 1880. Along with Seurat, Signac cofounded the Salon des Artistes Indépendants in 1884, and helped to further develop the Pointillist style of painting. The two artists began to fill their canvases with tiny dots of pure color using a precise, geometrical system rather than the previous methods employed by the early Impressionists. Signac was present at the Eighth Impressionist exhibition and also exhibited his works with Durand-Ruel in New York. He kept in close touch with fellow artists such as Pissarro and van Gogh, and also wrote articles on art criticism. The subject of this painting is Felix Feneon, a Parisian anarchist and art critic who was a friend of Paul Signac. *Portrait of Felix Feneon* currently resides in the collection of the Museum of Modern Art in New York.

Plate 59
ATANASIO SOLDATI (1896–1953)
Composition, 1950

Born in Italy in 1896, Atanasio Soldati served in World War
I from 1915 to 1918 before going on to study architecture
at the Accademia di Belle Arti in Parma. Influenced by
the work of Mauro Reggiani and Piet Mondrian, Soldati
began to gain a reputation for his painting in the 1930s
and joined the Parisian artists group, Abstraction-Création
in 1936. After the destruction of his Milan studio during
the Second World War, Soldati founded the Concrete
Art Movement, along with Gillo Dorfles, Gianni Monnet,
and Bruno Munari, in defiance of the state's aesthetic of
Socialist Realism. This painting is typical of Soldati's work
during the last years of his life, in which all of his subjects
are simplified to basic, geometric shapes

A cofounder of the group of Symbolist painters known as Les Nabis, Edouard Vuillard shared a studio with Bonnard and Denis. Strongly influenced by the work of Degas, Redon, and Gauguin, Vuillard carefully studied the canvases of the Impressionists. His garden scenes owe a great debt to the early paintings of Monet in his use of dappled sunlight. The sudden popularity of Japanese woodcuts had a profound effect on his compositions as well. Vuillard is best known, however, for his paintings of interiors, the bulk of which are impressively decorative domestic scenes executed with a keen sense of light and color. Vuillard produced numerous self-portraits throughout his career as an artist. This one is in the collection of the Musée d'Orsay in Paris.

Famous American
Masterpieces

Plate 61
GEORGE WESLEY BELLOWS (1882–1925)
Dempsey and Firpo, **1924**
Oil on canvas. 51 x 63¼ in.

Born in Columbus Ohio in 1882, George Wesley Bellows was an American realist painter who achieved notoriety for his vivid depictions of urban life in turn-of-the-century New York City. His themes often focused on the daily lives of the working-class, though he was also known for his satirical paintings that poked fun at the upper class. Bellows worked on *Dempsey and Firpo* for several months in 1923 and 1924. The painting depicts the famous 1923 fight in which U.S. heavyweight champion Jack Dempsey beat South American heavyweight champion Luis Angel Firpo, in a match that has been called the most savage two rounds in boxing history.

Plate 62
THOMAS HART BENTON (1889–1975)
Self-Portrait with Rita, 1922
Oil on canvas. 49½ x 40 in.

Thomas Hart Benton was an American painter in the Regionalist movement, known for his depictions of everyday life in middle America. Having declared himself an "enemy of modernism" in the early 1920s, Benton strove for a naturalistic style and is particularly remembered for his depictions of American life in the post-depression era. This painting depicts the artist and his wife Rita, sunbathing in Martha's Vineyard.

Plate 63
ALBERT BIERSTADT (1830–1902)
Emigrants Crossing the Plains, 1867
Oil on canvas. 67 x 102 in.

Born in Solingen, Germany in 1830, Albert Bierstadt emigrated to the United States as a young child, settling with his family in New Bedford, Massachusetts. Though he began his work painting in New England and New York, he is best known for his large, romantic landscapes of the American West. In this painting, Bierstadt depicts a group of settlers making the overland journey from the East to Oregon.

Plate 64
GEORGE CALEB BINGHAM (1811–1879)
Fur Traders Descending the Missouri, 1845
Oil on canvas. 29 x 37 in.

George Caleb Bingham was an American painter known for his beautiful, tranquil depictions of the American West. One of the best examples of Luminist style painters, Bingham primarily chose scenes from daily life on the Missouri frontier. Perhaps his most famous work, *Fur Traders Descending the Missouri* depicts a French trader rowing on the Missouri river with his half-Native American son.

Born in Pennsylvania, Cassatt was the only American female member of the Impressionists. She studied art at the Pennsylvania Academy of Art and then traveled to Europe, spending most of her life in Paris. Professionally, she was greatly influenced by her close friend, French Impressionist painter Edgar Degas. Cassatt painted family scenes of mothers and children, and achieved recognition for these tender representations. She was also very much influenced by Japanese woodcuts, and excelled in making woodcut prints. Her eyesight began to fail in 1900, and Cassatt stopped working by 1914. Like many of her paintings, this work depicts a mother and her child in a private moment of everyday life.

Admired for his portraits, landscapes, and everyday scenes, Chase was bom in Indiana and studied in Munich as a young man. After his return to the U.S., he gained a fine reputation as a painter and a teacher. Chase was particularly influenced by James McNeill Whistler, and even adopted that artist's flat, decorative style for a time. An excellent example of his early work, this painting depicts Miss Dora Wheeler, a textile designer who studied painting under Chase in New York City.

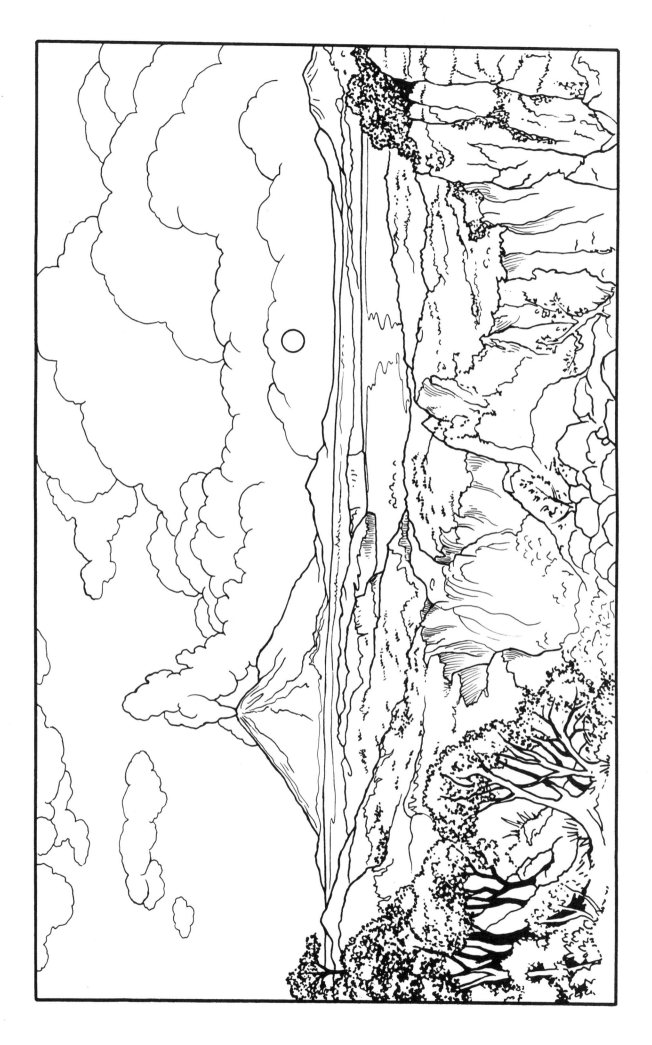

Plate 67
FREDERIC CHURCH (1826–1900)
Cotopaxi, 1862
Oil on canvas. 48 x 85 in.

Born in Hartford, Connecticut, Frederic Edwin Church studied under the great landscape painter Thomas Cole, and made his mark as part of the Hudson River School of American Landscape Painters. Though most of his contemporaries in the Hudson River School worked on local subjects, Church's work is noted for its romantic portrayal of landscapes in America and beyond. In Cotopaxi, Church depicts a smoldering volcano in Ecuador, set against a tranquil scene of South American countryside life.

Plate 68
THOMAS COLE (1801–1848)
Genesee Scenery
(Mountain Landscape with Waterfall), 1847
Oil on canvas. 51½ x 39¼ in.

Founder of the much-lauded Hudson River School of American Landscape Painters, Thomas Cole's work is known for its detailed and romanticized depiction of the American wilderness. Though he was born and raised in Lancashire, England, he did not begin painting until after his family emigrated to Ohio when he was seventeen. This painting depicts a bridge and mountain landscape on the Genesee river in upstate New York.

Plate 69
JOHN SINGLETON COPLEY (1738–1815)
Watson and the Shark, 1778
Oil on canvas. 71¾ x 90½ in.

Known mostly for his portraits, John Singleton Copley was an active and sought-after painter in both colonial America and England. Copley began his career early, painting his first portrait at the age of fourteen and becoming an admired professional portrait painter before turning twenty. The subject of this painting is the rescue of future London Mayor Brook Watson from a shark attack in Havana, Cuba when he was a 14 year-old cabin boy.

Plate 70
ASHER B. DURAND (1796–1886)
Kindred Spirits, **1849**
Oil on canvas. 46 x 36⅛ in.

Asher B. Durand, an American painter, engraver, and illustrator, was one of the founders of Hudson River School, a style of landscape painting that showcased the beauty of nature. He was among the first American painters to work directly from nature out-of-doors. The artist's legacy includes hundreds of breathtaking compositions depicting mainly the Adirondacks, the Catskills, and the White Mountains of New Hampshire. This painting—Durand's best-known work—shows his two friends, landscape painter Thomas Cole and poet William Cullen Bryant, in an intricately detailed forest setting in the Catskill Mountains in New York.

Plate 71
THOMAS EAKINS (1844–1916)
The Biglin Brothers Racing, 1873
Oil on canvas. 24 x 36 in.

Widely considered one of the most important artists in American history, Thomas Eakins was an American realist whose work centered on the lives and people of Philadelphia between 1870 and 1910. An amateur rower, Eakins painted dozens of scenes depicting different variations of the sport. This painting shows the Biglin Brothers of New York, national champions, rowing on the Schuylkill River during a trip to Philadelphia in the early 1870s.

Plate 72
WILLIAM GLACKENS (1870–1938)
Chez Mouquin, 1905
Oil on canvas. 48 x 39 in.

Born in Philadelphia, William Glackens studied at the Pennsylvania Academy of Fine Arts under the instruction of painter Robert Henri. Glackens was a member of the Ashcan school and was also one of "The Eight," a group of realist painters who exhibited their works together in 1908. Strongly influenced by the Impressionists, he painted subjects from everyday urban life as well as scenes of fashionable society. The subjects of this painting are Jeanne Lousie Mouquin and James B. Moore, who are depicted here in Jeanne Mouquin's restaurant, the Uptown Mouquin in New York City.

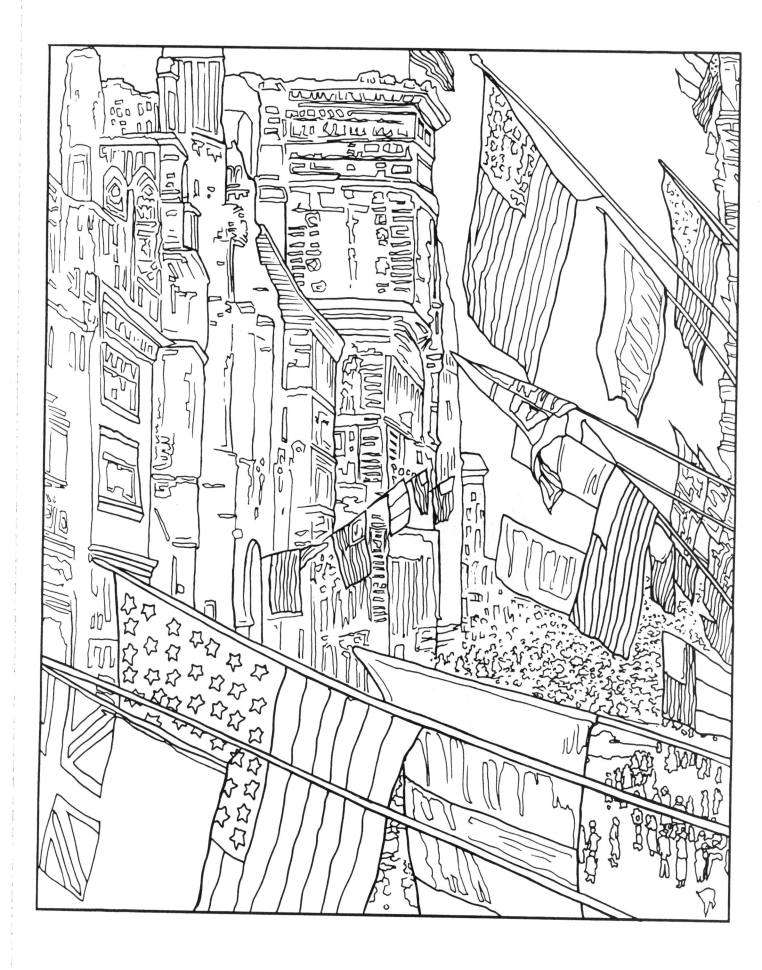

Plate 73
CHILDE HASSAM (1859–1935)
Allies Day, May 1917, 1917
Oil on canvas. 36¾ x 30¼ in.

A notable figure in the American Impressionist movement, Childe Hassam was often referred to as the "American Monet." Along with fellow artists such as William Merritt Chase and John Twachtman, Hassam formed the group known as The Ten American Painters. Their annual exhibitions greatly encouraged the spread of Impressionism and helped carry the art style into the twentieth century. This piece portrays Fifth Avenue in New York City while it was lined with flags during World War I.

Plate 74
EDWARD HICKS (1780–1849)
The Peaceable Kingdom, ca. 1837
Oil on canvas. 29 x 36 in.

A Pennsylvania sign painter and Quaker preacher, self-taught folk artist Edward Hicks is thought to have painted between 60 and 100 different versions of Peaceable Kingdom. The Peaceable Kingdom paintings were Hicks' interpretations of the biblical passage from Isaiah 11, which states that all men and beasts live in harmony. In the background of this painting, William Penn is pictured with others making a treaty with the Leni-Lenape Indians.

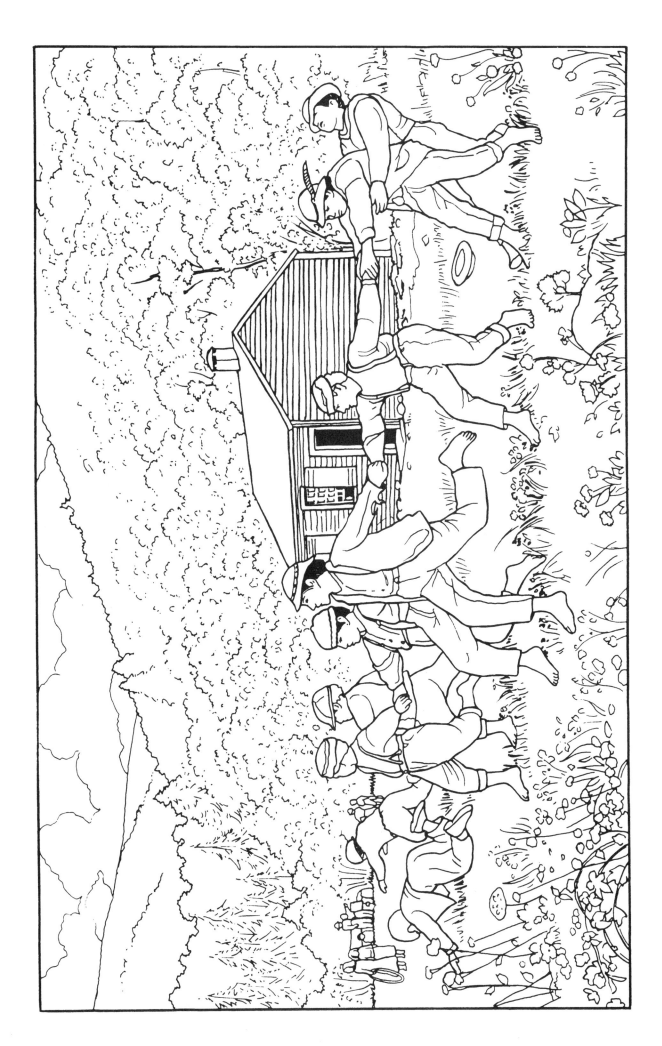

Plate 75
WINSLOW HOMER (1836–1910)
Snap the Whip, 1872
Oil on canvas. 22¼ x 36½ in.

Winslow Homer was one of America's most prominent realist painters. His attention to detail and fascination with subjects from everyday life came from his early experiences as a magazine illustrator during the Civil War. The boys in this picture are playing Snap the Whip, a recess game also known as Crack the Whip. To play, children hold hands in a long line and then run fast. The first ones in line stop suddenly, yanking the other kids sideways and causing the ones on the other end to break the chain and fall.

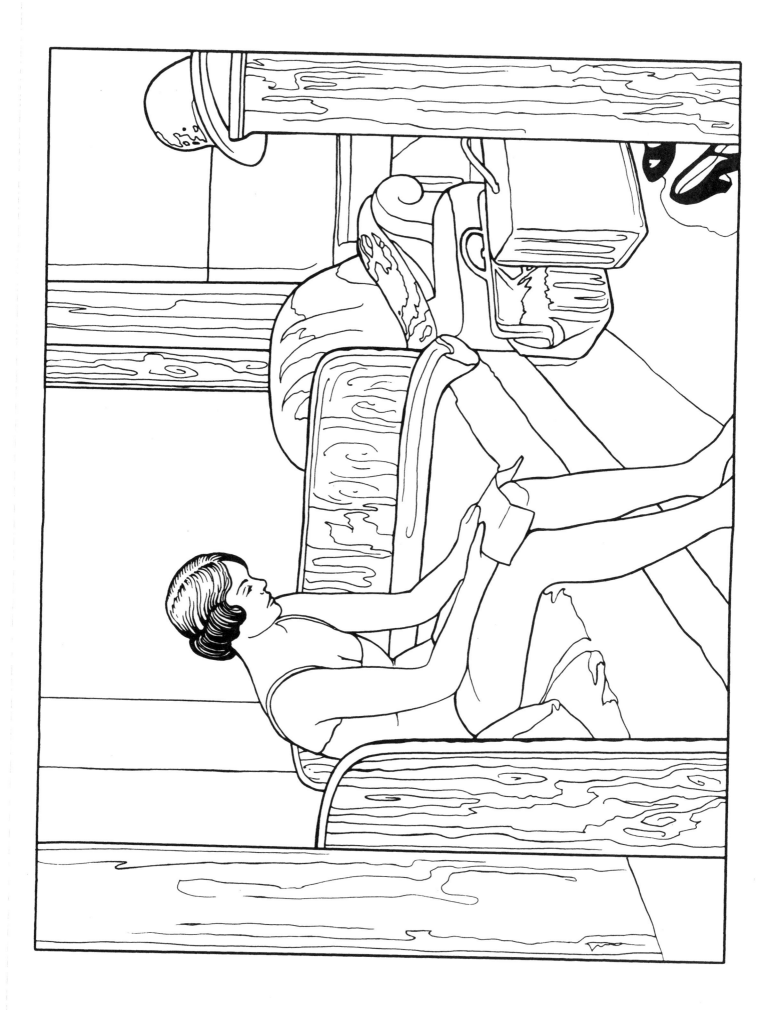

Twentieth-century Realist painter Edward Hopper is best known for his paintings that seem to emphasize the loneliness and alienation found in our society. Born in Nyack, New York, Hopper studied commercial art before switching his efforts to line art. He studied with Robert Henri, a member of the Ashcan school of painters, who typically painted scenes of city life. Hopper traveled to Europe three times between 1906 and 1910, but he remained unaffected by the avant-garde art movements burgeoning there. Taken as a whole, Hopper's work poignantly evokes the essence of American urban life. Like many of Hopper's figure paintings, *Hotel Room* depicts a woman alone in a room, and uses the painting's composition to emphasize her solitude.

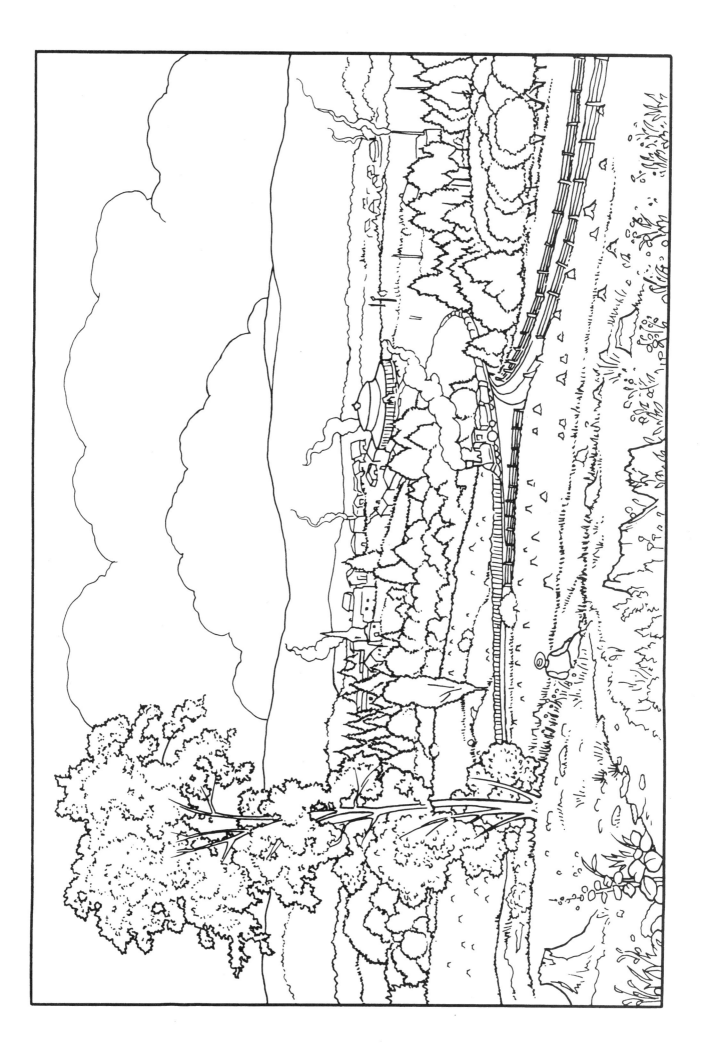

Plate 77
GEORGE INNESS (1825–1894)
The Lackawanna Valley, 1855
Oil on canvas. 34 x 50 in.

Often referred to as the "father of American landscape painting," the art of George Inness influenced generations of American painters. Best known for the sweeping landscapes he produced later in his career, his work was greatly influenced by the ideas of Swedish philosopher Emanuel Swedenborg. *The Lackawanna Valley* was created as a commission for the Delaware, Lackawanna, and Western Railroad. It depicts the railroad's first roundhouse in Scranton, Pennsylvania.

Plate 78
JONATHAN EASTMAN JOHNSON (1824–1906)
The Old Stagecoach, 1871
Oil on canvas. 36¼ x 60⅛ in.

Jonathan Eastman Johnson was an American painter best known for his depictions of everyday life in the nineteenth century, and his portraits of prominent Americans of the time. Known during his life as "The American Rembrandt," Johnson's portrait subjects included Abraham Lincoln, Nathaniel Hawthorne, Ralph Waldo Emerson, and Henry Wadsworth Longfellow. Although the setting of this painting came from a drawing Eastman made of an abandoned stagecoach in the Catskills, the children it depicts were staged by the artist on a platform in Nantucket.

Plate 79
EMANUEL LEUTZE (1816–1868)
Washington Crossing the Delaware, 1851
Oil on canvas. 149 in. x 255 in.

Among the most popular historical painters in mid-nineteenth-century America, Emanuel Leutze was born in Germany, but grew up in Philadelphia. His most famous work was *Washington Crossing the Delaware*, the first version of which was destroyed in a bombing raid during World War II. This version of the work, enormously popular in both America and Germany, was placed on exhibition in New York in 1851. Many studies for the painting still exist, as well as the engraving that was published in 1853 and circulated widely.

Plate 80
ALFRED MILLER (1810–1874)
Setting Traps for Beaver, 1837
Watercolor. 7⅞ in. x 10¼ in.

Although he was born in Baltimore, Maryland, and spent much of his career working in New Orleans, Alfred Jacob Miller is primarily remembered for his paintings of the American West, and of the Rocky Mountains in particular. Having studied with "The Romantics" in Paris, his paintings often reflect their romantic sensibilities in their portrayal of the American landscape. This painting depicts a pair of trappers setting five-pound traps in a river where they believe beavers are present.

Plate 81
GRANDMA MOSES (1860–1961)
Early Springtime on the Farm, 1945
Oil on canvas. 16 x 25¾ in.

One of the greatest folk painters of the twentieth century, Grandma Moses first began to paint at the age of seventy-eight. Born on a farm in Greenwich, New York, just before the Civil War, she primarily painted landscape scenes of country life. In 1939, her paintings were exhibited at the Museum of Modern Art in New York City. She produced 2,000 detailed paintings in all, some of which were used on Christmas cards and reproduced in prints. Grandma Moses died at the age of one hundred and one. The title of this painting is intended to be humorous, as it claims the scene to be "Early Springtime" in New England, while there is still a good deal of snow covering the landscape.

Plate 82
CHARLES WILLSON PEALE (1741–1827)
The Artist in His Museum, 1822
Oil on canvas. 103¾ x 79⅞ in.

Founder of Peale's American Museum in Philadelphia, Charles Willson Peale is best known for his portraits of leading figures from the American Revolution, which include Benjamin Franklin, John Hancock, Thomas Jefferson, George Washington, Alexander Hamilton, and many others. *The Artist in His Museum* is a nearly life-sized self-portrait, in which Peale depicts himself posing in the museum he founded.

Plate 83
MAURICE PRENDERGAST (1858–1924)
Central Park, ca. 1908–10
Oil on canvas. 20¾ x 27 in.

Born in St. John's, Newfoundland, Canada, Maurice Prendergast grew up in Boston, and returned there as an adult to set up an art studio. In the early 1890s, he traveled abroad to study art in both Paris and Italy and was particularly inspired by Post-Impressionism. He developed his own signature style of blocks of color and dark outlines, creating mosaic or stained glass-like effects in his paintings and watercolors. Central Park is a typical example of the artist's many scenes of people gathered in New York or by the seaside.

Plate 84
FREDERIC REMINGTON (1861–1909)
A Dash for the Timber, **1889**
Oil on canvas. 48½ x 84⅛ in.

Famous for his depictions of the nineteenth-century American West, Frederic Remington's favorite subjects included action scenes of Native Americans, cowboys, and the U.S. cavalry. Remington left college in order to travel across the U.S., working as a cowboy and prospector, while filling a journal with observations and that he would later use in his paintings. This painting, which depicts a group of cowboys in a gunfight with Native Americans, launched Remington's career as a major artist when it was exhibited at the National Academy in 1889.

JOHN SINGER SARGENT (1856–1925)
Paul Helleu Sketching with His Wife, 1889
Oil on canvas. 26⅛ x 32⅛ in.

Portrait painter John Singer Sargent was born in Florence, Italy, to American parents. As a child, Sargent traveled with his parents around Europe, and gained experiences that would contribute greatly to his self-assurance with all kinds of people and places. Exquisite portrayals of affluent figures of the day and their families made Sargent a much sought-after artist, and many patrons clamored for his refined, flattering style. Sargent went through a brief Impressionist phase, inspired by the work of Claude Monet at Giverny. In this painting, Sargent employs the French *plein air* technique, depicting Paul Helleu and his wife in natural light when they visited him in the countryside.

Plate 86
GILBERT STUART (1755–1828)
George Washington, 1795
Oil on canvas. 29¼ x 24 in.

Known as one of America's greatest portrait painters, Gilbert Stuart created over 1,000 portraits throughout the course of his career, including portraits of the first six Presidents of the United States. His most famous work is an unfinished portrait of George Washington, which appeared on the one-dollar bill for over a century. This painting of George Washington is one of eighteen similar portraits, with the first most likely painted from life and the rest created as copies of the original.

Plate 87
BENJAMIN WEST (1738–1820)
Colonel Guy Johnson, 1775
Oil on canvas. 79¾ x 54½ in.

Known mostly for his paintings of historical scenes around the time of the American Revolution, Benjamin West was one of the first American artists to receive an international reputation. Though he was born in rural Pennsylvania, West would spend most of his life living in England, where he eventually founded the Royal Academy. The subjects of this portrait are military officer and diplomat Guy Johnson and Mohawk chief Karanghyontye.

Plate 88
JAMES MCNEILL WHISTLER (1834–1903)
Portrait of the Artist's Mother, 1871
Oil on canvas. 56¾ x 64 in.

American painter and etcher James Abbott McNeill Whistler was born in Lowell, Massachusetts. He spent his childhood in Russia, where his father worked as a civil engineer. In 1855, Whistler traveled to Paris to study art and remained in Europe for the rest of his life. During the 1860s, Whistler developed a fascination with Japanese art, and began to incorporate Oriental fans and blossoms into his paintings. A propagandist of the "art for art's sake" philosophy, Whistler believed that painting should exist for its own sake without conveying literary or moral ideas. In his later years, Whistler, who worked in watercolors, pastels, and executed more than fifty etchings, came to be regarded as a major artist of refreshing originality as well as a champion of modern art. Arguably Whistler's most famous painting, *Portrait of the Artist's Mother* would become an icon in American art, receiving its own postage stamp in 1934 that bore the slogan, "In Memory and in Honor of the Mothers of America."

Born in Iowa, Grant Wood asked his dentist and his sister to pose as a farmer and his unmarried daughter for what has become one of the most famous (and most parodied) paintings in the history of American art, *American Gothic.* Although Wood was accused of ridiculing the narrow-mindedness of rural life, he denied the allegation, insisting that his painting was not a caricature of rural America, but a celebration of the values of the Midwest. The painting's title is derived from the Gothic Revival style of the cottage in the background.

Plate 90
N. C. WYETH (1882–1945)
Nothing Would Escape, 1911
Oil on canvas. 46½ x 37½ in.

Considered one of America's greatest illustrators, N.C. Wyeth was also a respected and accomplished painter. Born in Needham, Massachusetts in 1882, Wyeth's career took off from an early age, with his first commissioned illustration coming from the *Saturday Evening Post* at a mere 21 years old. Throughout the course of his life he would illustrate 112 books and create over 3000 paintings. This work is typical of Wyeth in its dramatic depiction of Native Americans. It first appeared in the November 1911 issue of *Harper's Monthly Magazine*.